Handel the Philanthropist

The Foundling Museum
London

FOUNDLING
HOSPITAL.
75   *Wilson, 1746.*

GERALD COKE
Handel
COLLECTION

THE
foundling
MUSEUM

First published by the Foundling Museum on the occasion of the exhibition *Handel the Philanthropist*, 16 January – 28 June 2009 to mark the 250th anniversary of Handel's death.

Handel and the Foundling Hospital by Donald Burrows first published in *Music and Letters*, 1977, © Donald Burrows 1977, 2009

40 Brunswick Square
London WC1N 1AZ
www.foundlingmuseum.org.uk
020 7841 3600

ISBN 978-0-9551808-3-5

Printed by BAS Printers

Contents

Director's Foreword

The Foundling Museum is delighted to present Handel the Philanthropist in which we celebrate the life and charitable work of the Foundling Hospital's great benefactor George Frideric Handel. The exhibition commemorates the 250th anniversary of the composer's death, bringing together a rich collection of works of art, manuscripts and other artefacts reflecting the diversity of the Museum's own collections.

Such an exhibition could not have been realised without the support of many people, from those who have graciously agreed to lend valuable items from their own collections to donors who have financially supported the exhibition and its related events. I am also grateful for the dedication of Katharine Hogg and Colin Coleman who have worked so hard organising the show, assisted by the rest of the Museum team. The collaboration of the Gerald Coke Handel Foundation has been crucial for the success of the project and we are very grateful to the Trustees for their steadfast support.

2009 will see a host of Handel-related events around the world and I am pleased that the Foundling Museum will play a major part in celebrating the life and times of this great Baroque composer.

Lars Tharp
Director

Acknowledgements

The exhibition has been made possible with funding from the Gerald Coke Handel Foundation and the generous assistance of many individuals and institutions. We are grateful to the staff of the Royal Collection, the British Library, Coram, the National Portrait Gallery, Leeds Library and Information Services, King's College, Cambridge, The Royal College of Music, The Royal Academy of Music, the Royal Society of Musicians of Great Britain and the Handel House Museum for their generous assistance with loans from their collections. David Tennant and Sally Bevan from the London Metropolitan Archives gave valuable assistance and Professor Donald Burrows kindly revised his article on 'Handel and the Foundling Hospital' for us to include in this publication.

The recorded performance of *Messiah* which accompanies the exhibits is by kind permission of The Sixteen. Much of the preparation of exhibits was carried out by Francisco Mora Andrés, for which we are grateful. Colleagues at the Foundling Museum have offered support in all areas of the project. Particular thanks are due to Clara Dutton for the design and preparation of this catalogue, and to Colin Coleman for his indefatigable contribution at all stages of the project.

Katharine Hogg
Curator

George Frideric Handel (1685-1759) by the school of Thomas Hudson (1701-1779)

Handel the Philanthropist

Katharine Hogg

George Frideric Handel was a leading musician of his day, a composer, performer and entrepreneur who weathered periods of financial difficulty in his professional life and shared the benefits of his successes. He settled in London early in his career and worked for many different patrons including the Royal household, as well as running his own opera productions and concert series, and collaborating in various business ventures. Handel favoured two charities in particular; the Fund for Decay'd Musicians (now the Royal Society of Musicians) and the Foundling Hospital, which both benefited from charity concerts and from bequests in his will.

Handel's relationship with the Foundling Hospital and with the Society for the Support of Decay'd Musicians developed during the last two decades of his life, when he was enjoying prosperity after a period of financial uncertainty. Benefit concerts were a popular form of fundraising for individuals and institutions, and Handel's music remains particularly associated with charitable performances to this day.

Handel and the Foundling Hospital

In May 1749 Handel approached the Hospital to offer a benefit concert to fund the completion of the Chapel. The General Committee minutes of Thursday 4 May record:

> *Mr Handel being present and having generously and charitably offered a performance of vocal and instrumental music to be held at this Hospital, and that the money arising therefrom should be applied to the finishing the chapel of the Hospital Resolved — That the thanks of this Committee be returned to Mr Handel for this his generous and charitable offer.*

Extract from the third codicil to Handel's will with a bequest to the Foundling Hospital

Handel may have learnt of the need for funds to complete the Chapel from his publisher, John Walsh, who had already become a Governor of the Hospital. The concert took place three weeks after Handel's offer to the Committee, and was a great success. It was attended by the Prince and Princess of Wales, attracted a full house and raised over £350. Handel composed a new work for the occasion, the anthem *Blessed are they that considereth the poor*, popularly known as the 'Foundling Hospital anthem'. This work borrows music from various earlier works, finishing with the 'Hallelujah' chorus from *Messiah*, which would hardly have been known to London audiences, as there had been only a handful of performances since its first performance in Dublin in 1742.

The concert included Handel's *Music for the Royal Fireworks* and the anthem *How beautiful are the feet*, which had been composed to celebrate the peace following the Austrian War of Succession. These works had been first performed in April that year, and the concert also included extracts from *Solomon* which had been a new oratorio during that season. Handel's selection of movements on the subject of the building of Solomon's temple was appropriate for a fund-raising concert for the chapel, which had been structurally completed but still lacked furniture and windows.

Messiah at the Foundling Hospital

Handel's name was put forward to be a Hospital Governor after his offer of a concert in 1749, but he declined the invitation; the minutes report that

> *the Secretary acquainted the Committee that Mr. Handel called upon him last Saturday, and returned his thanks to the Committee for the Honour intended him of being a Governor of this Hospital; But he desired to be excused therefrom that he should serve the Charity with more Pleasure in his way, than being a member of the Corporation.*

Handel continued to serve the charity "in his way"; following the success of the first concert the governors asked him to put on another performance the following year, and he chose to perform *Messiah*.

The oratorio had been first performed in Dublin in 1742; an advertisement in Faulkner's Dublin Journal announced the performance 'For the Relief of Prisoners in the several Gaols, and for the Support of Mercer's Hospital ... and of the Charitable Infirmary'. However, following its success in Dublin the oratorio had not been well received by London audiences; its few performances had been overshadowed by a debate over whether it was appropriate to perform a work with so sacred a subject in a theatre, a venue more commonly associated with worldly interests.

The performance of *Messiah* in 1750 for a charitable purpose, the Foundling Hospital, appeared to resolve this difficulty; the concert was oversubscribed, and the minutes note that the High Constable and his assistants were to be asked to attend to keep gate-crashers out. There were double-bookings for the first performance in May, when tickets were sold at the door as well as in advance, and Handel attended a further meeting at the Hospital, when a second performance was hastily arranged for a fortnight later, to accommodate the ticket-holders who had been turned away.

Handel was duly elected a Governor of the Hospital in 1750, although he had at first refused the invitation. He donated the first organ for the Hospital chapel, and remained in close contact, advising the Governors on the concert for the formal opening of the Chapel in 1753, and approving the appointment of the organist in the following year. A misunderstanding between the Foundling Hospital and the composer in 1754, when the Hospital thought that Handel had given them ownership of rights over all *Messiah* performances, led to some harsh

✥

words from the composer; however, the relationship survived and four months later Handel gave his annual performance in the Chapel. He continued to give benefit performances of *Messiah* every year until his death in 1759, raising almost £7,000 for the charity. These performances established *Messiah* as a central work in the English repertoire.

The Fund for the Support of Decay'd Musicians

In 1738 three musicians working at the King's Theatre in the Haymarket recognised two destitute children in the street as the family of an oboist named Kytch, who had died suddenly and left his family penniless. The musicians were the violinist and composer Michael Christian Festing, the flautist Carl Weideman, who later taught George III, and a Mr Vincent, who is thought to have played the bassoon. They were inspired to do something to help musicians and their families in distress, and advertised a meeting on 23 April 1738 for the "Subscribers to a Fund for the Support of Decay'd Musicians or their families" at the Crown and Anchor Tavern.

After further meetings 228 musicians, including Handel, put their names to the Declaration of Trust on 28 August 1739. The subscription was 2/6d a quarter or 10/- a year, generating about £150 for distribution among claimants. Unemployment was not sufficient grounds to receive funds, although often elderly performers were helped if they had been summarily dismissed from their jobs. There was no welfare state at that time, so that illness, the loss of a finger or even of teeth could quickly leave a professional musician destitute. London offered employment for musicians in theatres, pleasure gardens, churches and cathedrals, and had a large population of musicians from home and abroad.

Detail from the Declaration of Trust of the Society of Musicians,© The Royal Society of Musicians of Great Britain

The nobility and gentry gave support and some became Honorary Subscribers, their names heading the Annual Lists of which the earliest known extant copy is dated 1742. Meetings were held in various Coffee Houses or Public Houses in London until 1809, when the Society obtained premises in Lisle Street, where it remained until 1931 when it moved to Stratford Place. The Society gradually acquired funds which were invested to provide income, so that it no longer relies only on the subscriptions of its Members. The present annual membership subscription for the 1,400 members is £25 a year, although many give annual amounts as additional donations.

Handel and the Society for Decay'd Musicians

In March 1739 Handel gave his first benefit concert for the Society at the King's Theatre, providing both the theatre and his direction of the performance at no charge. He chose the oratorio *Alexander's Feast*, composed two years earlier, which had just been published in score. The audience was described as 'numerous and polite' and although tickets were given out at no charge, many people made donations for the charity.

Handel appeared at several further concerts for the Society; Charles Burney wrote that 'he seldom was absent from the benefit for Decayed Musicians'. Performances included *Acis and Galatea* in 1740, *Parnasso in Festa* in 1741 and various vocal and instrumental works in the following years. In March 1752 the last item in the concert was 'A Grand Concerto of Mr Handel's' and the following year the benefit concert took place on 30 April, the day before the Foundling Hospital *Messiah* performance, which Handel directed.

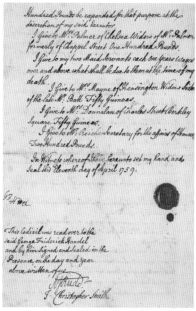

The last codicil to Handel's will, written a few days before he died

In the last codicil to his will, written a few days before his death in 1759, Handel bequeathed £1,000 to the Society, a huge donation which was unmatched for many years. A performance of Handel's *Messiah* was given by Members of the Society almost every year for the Society's benefit from 1760 until 1914; occasionally another work was substituted.

William Russell, organist at the Foundling Hospital and member of the Royal Society of Musicians

The son of the organ builder Hugh Russell, and his wife Elizabeth, William was born on 6 October 1777 and baptised on 26 October at St Andrew's Holborn where the celebrated composer John Stanley was organist.

Russell first applied for the post of organist at the Foundling Hospital in 1798, along with seven others including the famous organists Samuel Wesley and Thomas Sanders Dupuis. The relatively unknown John Immyns (1764-?1818) was appointed, but had to resign in 1801 after various complaints about his conduct. Immyns asked Russell to fill the ensuing vacancy until the Governors could elect a new organist, and it appears that he so impressed the Governors that he was recommended by the General Committee for the post at the next meeting of the General Court on 1 April.

William applied for membership of the Royal Society of Musicians in 1802, signing his application form on 3 October; one of the witnesses was John Immyns. His application states that he

> *has studied and practised music for a livelihood upwards of seven years, Composer and piano forte player at Sadlers Wells, plays the piano forte at Covent Garden Theatre, teaches the Piano Forte – Organist of St Anns Limehouse and the Foundling Hospital, twenty five years of age, is a single man.*

He was admitted to the Society on 6 March 1803; he married his wife Mary Ann before 1810, but died in 1813 leaving his wife and two children in difficult financial circumstances.

Minutes and accounts in the Society's archive note that Russell's widow applied for financial assistance in February 1814. Her application was favourably received with the funeral expenses covered (£8) and she received the widow's allowance until her death in 1854, as well as money for the children's schooling. Her daughter, Mary Ann, was apprenticed to study music with Sarah Jennings, who had previously been a pupil of Russell.

In addition to these benefactions William's widow applied to the Society on behalf of her son, also William. The Minutes of the Governors Meeting of 2 July 1826 record this application but give no details of the proposal mentioned:

> *Mrs Russell attended and inform'd the board that her Son William would be 14 years of age the 16th of Septr. next, and that a situation can be found, which after two years would prove lucrative to him, she solicited the usual apprentice permission for the purpose of making him competent for the same.*

> *The Governors taking this proposition into consideration ordered the following letter to be written and forwarded to her:*

> *Madam,*
> *I am instructed by the Govrs. of the R.S. of Musicians to inform you, they have considered your proposal relative to your Son, and from the very*

desirable prospect you have in view for him, they have resolved to meet your wishes when he has attain'd his 14th year upon your giving a sufficient acknowledgement that he will then have no further claim in the Society I remain &c Mr Simcock, Secretary.

Ticket for Messiah at the Birmingham Musical Festival, 1811

The Russell family's story reflects that of many musicians and their families, who fell on hard times with the death or ill-health of the family's only income earner, and demonstrates the important role played by the Society in rescuing families from poverty and offering practical support for the long term.

The Handel Commemoration Concerts in 1784

In 1784 the Handel Commemoration concerts took place in Westminster Abbey and the Pantheon in Oxford Street, to mark the 25th anniversary of Handel's death and the centenary of his birth, which in the old-style calendar was 1684, as recorded on his monument in Westminster Abbey. These large-scale performances involved around 500 musicians, many of whom were Members of the Royal Society of Musicians, and proceeds from the performances were advertised as for the benefit of the Society. Organised by Sir Watkin Williams Wynn, Joah Bates and Viscount Fitzwilliam, the festival performers included such distinguished soloists of the time as Madame Mara, Thomas Norris and Samuel Harrison. The concerts attracted an audience of 4,500 and many descriptions of the event survive; of these perhaps the best known is *An Account of the Musical Performances in Westminster-Abbey, and the Pantheon … in Commemoration of Handel*, by Charles Burney, published in 1785 'for the Benefit of the Musical Fund'.

The concerts raised £6,000 for the Society and £1,000 for the Westminster Hospital, and all five performances were attended by King George III, who took an interest in the Society and gave it permission to be renamed as The Royal Society of Musicians. He commanded the Concert of Antient Music, an institution which promoted the performance of older music, to give an annual performance of *Messiah* for the Society's benefit after its twelve subscription concerts each year, and granted the Royal Charter in 1790. The Commemoration concerts of 1784 were the first of several Handel festivals which benefited the Royal Society of Musicians in the years which followed.

❖

Handel's legacy

In the third codicil to his will Handel wrote 'I give a fair copy of the Score and all the parts of my Oratorio called The Messiah to the Foundling Hospital'; the provision of a set of performing parts would enable the benefit concerts to continue after the composer's death. Handel died on 14 April 1759 and the parts were duly copied out under the direction of John Christopher Smith senior, Handel's assistant, and delivered to the Hospital. Smith had organised the performers for the *Messiah* performances during Handel's lifetime, and his son of the same name was appointed organist of the Foundling Hospital in 1754. The annual performances of *Messiah* continued until 1777; revenues dwindled in the 1770s and may have led to the lack of impetus for arranging further performances. After Handel's death the annual *Messiah* concerts were organised by John Christopher Smith junior and the oboist William Teede took care of the business arrangements; he was later to petition the Royal Society of Musicians for assistance due to his failing health.

While Handel's music is his greatest bequest, his philanthropic work in donating performances for needy causes also established a lasting legacy. Performances of his works, in particular of *Messiah*, for charitable causes have taken place throughout the 19th and 20th centuries, and continue to this day. As well as the Handel Commemoration concerts in the 18th century which raised considerable sums for the Royal Society of Musicians, performances of Handel's music were particularly associated with benefit concerts at St Paul's Cathedral for the Sons of the Clergy, and for several hospitals and infirmaries. In 1834 the Handel Commemoration in Westminster Abbey was revived and the funds raised were shared between the Royal Society of Musicians, the New Musical Fund, the Choral Fund and the Royal Academy of Music. Many provincial choral festivals were established in the 19th century and benefited local charities, such as the Birmingham Triennial Musical Festival which supported the Birmingham General Hospital, and these festivals included Handel's works almost without exception.

Hofpital for the Maintenance and Education of expofed and deferted young Children.

THIS is to give Notice, that towards the Support of this Charity, the Sacred Oratorio, called,

M E S S I A H,

Will be performed in the Chapel of this Hofpital, under the Direction of George Frederick Handel, Efq; on Thurfday next, the 27th inft. at twelve o'clock at Noon precifely; and, to prevent the Chapel being crouded, no more Tickets will be delivered than it can conveniently hold; which are ready to be had of the Steward of the Hofpital; at *Arthur's Chocolate-houfe* in *St. James's Street*; at *Batfon's Coffee-houfe* in *Corn-bill*; and at *Tom's Coffee-houfe* in *Devereux Court*, at Half a Guinea each.   T. COLLINGWOOD, Secretary.

Advertisement for performance of Messiah at the Foundling Hospital on 27 April 1758, in Lloyd's Evening Post and British Chronicle

✤

Interior view of the Foundling Hospital chapel from the sanctuary,
hand-coloured lithograph ca.1830 © Gerald Coke Handel Foundation

Handel and the Foundling Hospital

Donald Burrows

Handel's association with the Foundling Hospital lasted almost exactly ten years, from the preparations for the Hospital's benefit concert in May 1749 until his death, and his music remained an important force in the life of the Hospital for some time afterwards. The surviving records of the Hospital enable us to trace his relationship with the institution, and also provide clues about his situation as his blindness developed during the years 1751-4.[1] His connection with the Hospital largely concerns performances of *Messiah*, but two other performances in the Chapel of the Hospital with which he was directly involved also call for consideration, since they raise questions about the textual history of the Foundling Hospital Anthem.

❖

Handel's entrance into the life of the Hospital came at a critical moment in its history. The number of children the Hospital wished to receive was expanding rapidly, the Chapel was not finished, and the building of the residential east wing was about to commence. His first Foundling Hospital performance, a concert, was given in the Chapel before it had glass in the windows and before it received many of its final furnishings, hence the need for the reassurance in the advertisement that the Chapel would be 'Sashed and made commodious'. It seems likely that the concert came about through the music publisher John Walsh the younger. Walsh was elected a Governor of the Hospital in 1748 and attended the Court meeting on 28 December to pay his donation of £50, at which meeting he would have heard about the Hospital's growing financial commitments: the Governors were anxious to finish the Chapel properly 'although it may exceed the money received'.[2] Walsh probably came away from the meeting with the idea of approaching Handel for a musical performance, doubtless stimulated by both altruism and the feeling that it would be a good advertisement for all concerned. There are no references to the concert in the minute books of the Hospital until Handel turned up to the Committee meeting on 4 May 1749,[3] but unofficial discussions must have taken place before that date. The programme was known at the meeting, and the date of the performance was fixed for Wednesday 24 May at 11.00 a.m. A week later, when presumably it was known that some royal presence was expected, the date was moved back to the 23rd by the Committee to avoid the clash with Prince George's birthday, but the Court meeting the same day changed the date to Thursday the 25th and the time to noon. On the 19th a letter was received by the Secretary 'signifying the desire of His Royal Highness the Prince of Wales for deferring Mr. Handel's performance to Saturday the 27th Instant' and the Sub-committee hurriedly complied.[4] The Court had given instructions at their meeting that the following should be added to the advertisements:

N.B. There will be no collection [the tickets were half a guinea] and Mr. Tonson having printed the words of this performance for the benefit of this Charity, Books may be had at the Places where Tickets are delivered and at one Shilling each.

George Frideric Handel, terracotta bust by Louis François Roubiliac (1695-1762)
© Coram in the care of the Foundling Museum

Jacob Tonson had been elected a Governor in 1742 and was presumably in close contact with the Hospital's affairs; it is perhaps unlikely that he had printed the word book by 10 May, and from the fact that the title page carries 25 May as the performance date we may infer that it was prepared between 10 and 20 May.

The records of the Hospital tell us that 1,300 tickets were printed and an unspecified number for the orchestra, though a newspaper reference stated that 'above one hundred voices and performers have been engaged'. Handel's specifications for the wind parts on the *Fireworks Music*, which opened the programme, call for more than 50 players but this is an open-air scoring and for the Chapel performance Handel doubtless reduced the wind and included string players. The Anthem on the Peace (*How beautiful are the feet*, HWV 266) followed, presumably with the original soloists: Bayly and Mence (altos) and 'The Boy'.[5] The extracts from *Solomon* that comprised part two of the programme[6] demand alto, tenor and bass soloists, who were probably those of the original production a couple of months before: Galli, Lowe and Reinhold.

The conducting score of the oratorio was used in the preparations for the concert: after the chorus 'Praise the Lord with Harp and Tongue' the word 'Fine' appears,[7] and it is possible that some of the cuts in this movement were made for the Foundling Hospital. The new Foundling Hospital Anthem (*Blessed are they that considereth the poor*, HWV 268), which formed the final part of the programme, will be considered below. Though the newspapers mention an audience of 'above a thousand', the proceeds recorded do not bear this out.[8] Nevertheless, the occasion seems to have been successful for all concerned, especially since the Prince and Princess of Wales expressed their satisfaction with the performance.[9]

As the glazing, plastering and paving of the Chapel proceeded later in the year, the Governors turned their minds towards an official opening for the completed building. The Sub-committee had resolved at one of its first meetings that the children should attend Divine Service on Sundays, but the attentions of the Governors were also directed towards attracting a congregation from outside. For the next stage in events, some of the relevant documents must be quoted in full.

7 February 1749/50
Resolved:
That the Workmen employed in the Chapel be acquainted that it is to be opened on Tuesday the first of May Next, and it is expected that their works be Severally completed before Saturday the 28th of April.
Resolved:
That it be referred to the Sub Committee to consider of the Manner of Opening the Chapel: and having a Performance of Musick, and that they do Consult Mr. Handel thereupon.[10]

❖

The Sub-committee (14 February) duly set about the preparation of the plates (presumably with Handel's knowledge) for an admission ticket, which read:

> On Thursday the 3rd of May 1750 there will be a Grand Performance of Vocal and Instrumental Musick under the Composure [sic] and Direction of George Frederick Handel Esq. It being the Opening of the Chapel.[11]

It should be noted that there is no mention of a service: perhaps another mixed concert was contemplated. However, at their next meeting (21 February) the General Committee resolved:

> That the Chapel of this Hospital be opened for the Performance of a Divine Service upon Thursday the third Day of May next; And That His Grace the Archbishop of Canterbury be requested to preach a Sermon therein on that Occasion.[12]

Handel must have been informed of, or been a party to, such a change of plan: but a fortnight later the Committee

> Reconsidered the Resolution about opening the Chapel on Thursday the 3rd of May next with a Sermon and
> *Resolved*:
> That the Sermon be Postponed.
> *Resolved*:
> That the Secretary do wait upon Mr. Handel to propose a Performance of Musick and Voices in the Chapel on Tuesday the first of May next.[13]

It may have happened that the plan for a service with sermon had not found favour with the Archbishop or Handel. It seems much more likely, however, that the Committee had come to realise what 'opening the Chapel' involved. A clergyman would have to be appointed to look after the routine services, to baptise and catechise the children, and eventually a regular organist would be needed as well. The Hospital at that stage had no way of financing such permanent officers, and the Governors could not foresee a regular income from annual musical performances. Nevertheless, the interest aroused by the 1749 concert clearly needed to be followed up, and Handel came to produce *Messiah* on the first occasion for the Hospital not for the opening of the Chapel, but for the opening of the organ, which he had presented to the Chapel. This was an excuse rather than a reason for the performance, though the reputation of Handel's organ playing might have been such as to make some appeal to public imagination. The organ itself was not finished in time, and its maintenance subsequently gave the Hospital considerable trouble.[14]

✦

The first performance of *Messiah* at the Hospital on 1 May 1750 was successful; embarrassingly so for the organisers (see the Appendix). The Subcommittee had worked out the arrangements for the performance thoroughly enough,[15] but more people presented themselves than the Chapel could hold. A repeat performance was held on 15 May, advertised with assurances that the Hospital would correctly calculate the capacity of the Chapel this time. Again a substantial audience turned out, and the performances taken together brought the Hospital nearly £1,000 after expenses had been paid. In future years the Committee limited the issue of tickets to 1,200 instead of the 1,500 that had been prepared originally, but on some later occasions that number was exceeded: presumably the permanent furniture of the Chapel, when installed, was able to cope with larger numbers. Between the two performances Handel was elected a Governor of the Hospital (an honour that he had declined the year before) without having to pay the customary £50 donation. Following the success with *Messiah* it is not surprising that the Hospital contacted Handel again before the end of the year for another 'Performance of Sacred Musick'. He rejected the idea of a February performance, and eventually the same pattern of well-attended double performances was repeated in April and May 1751.[16] In both years Bernard Gates is recorded as returning some of the money paid for the Chapel Royal boys,[17] but there is only one other mention of him in later years,[18] and it seems that from 1752 William Boyce was in charge of the boys, although Gates did not resign the Mastership in favour of James Nares until 1757.

Extract from the minutes of the General Committee of the Foundling Hospital, 2 May 1750, reproduced by permission of Coram courtesy of the London Metropolitan Archive

With the Chapel now nearly finished and considerably more funds available, the Hospital turned back to the matter of an official opening. On 17 July 1751 the Sub-committee

> *Recommended*
> to the General Committee to consider of a Time for Opening the Chapel, and the steps to be taken previous thereto; especially with respect to Mr. Handell.[19]

1751 was the year of *Jephtha*, the oratorio whose composition Handel had to lay aside between February and June because of trouble with his eyesight. The

❖

performers' account for the second *Messiah* performance of 1751 did not reach the Committee until 1 October, and uncertainties over Handel's situation may have prevented the Committee from proceeding until 16 October, when they

Resolved:
That it is the Opinion of this Committee, That the opening of the Chapel of this Hospital, be on Thursday the 5th of December next and that Mr. Handel be desir'd to direct such Musical Performances therein, on that day, as he shall think proper, to be Rehearsed on the Tuesday before.[20]

The Foundling Hospital, 1746 by Richard Wilson
© Coram in the care of the Foundling Museum

At the same time they resolved again to approach the Archbishop of Canterbury to ask him for a sermon on that occasion. However, soon afterwards the date was postponed, and twelve months passed during which *Messiah* was performed again, a contract for maintaining the organ was arranged, and a serious search was made for a minister for the Chapel. Only a single performance of *Messiah* was given in 1752, and although it was as successful as before there is no mention of any intention of a repeat performance in the minutes. This may have been due to Handel's declining health and a perception that the Hospital would be relying on him for an extra contribution at the opening of the Chapel.

On 25 October 1752 the Committee returned to the problem of the Chapel opening, setting the date for Thursday 28 December, determining to contact Handel, Boyce and Smith, deciding that entry to the opening would be by printed ticket, and providing for the subsequent routine life of the Chapel – prayers were to be read twice every Sunday and a sermon was to be preached every Sunday morning.[21] In November the stipend for the Reader was fixed at £40 and a suitable candidate was found in John Waring, but on 6 December the Committee had to resolve

That the Opening of the Chapel in this Hospital be postponed to Friday the Second day of February next, being the Purification of the Blessed Virgin Mary.[22]

The Sub-committee considered ticket arrangements for the occasion and reported back,[23] but further consideration was postponed pending the provision

✥

of a bishop to preach the sermon. On 28 March 1753 the Court heard that the Bishop of Worcester had agreed to preach, and that the music was to be 'an Anthem Te Deum and Jubilate composed by George Frederick Handel Esqr ... performed under his Direction'.[24] The Chapel finally received its official opening on Monday 16 April at 11.00 a.m. In addition to the Te Deum, Jubilate and Anthem on this occasion, the advertisement for the Chapel opening mentions that the Coronation Anthem (presumably 'Zadok the Priest') was performed after the sermon.

In the Sub-committee draft of this advertisement the words 'under his Direction' have been deleted from the notice of the music.[25] Perhaps not too much significance should be attached to this, but there is no doubt that Handel's increasing blindness was one of the causes of the later postponements of the Chapel opening. Less than a week before the opening, the Committee wrote to Handel expressing concern over something that they had read in the newspapers:[26] the original newspaper reference had been as follows:

> On Monday se'nnight the new Chapel at the Foundling Hospital will be preach'd in, for the first Time, by the Lord Bishop of Worcester; at the same Time will be performed an Anthem under the Direction of Mr. Handel, for the Benefit of the said Hospital. And we hear that that Gentleman is composing a Funeral Anthem for himself, to be performed (when it shall please God to take him hence) in the above-mentioned Chapel, for the Benefit of the Charity.[27]

It is very unlikely that Handel was composing anything new by April 1753, but enough has been given above to show that, on at least two occasions while Handel's sight was still adequate, he was approached with specific proposals about the opening of the Chapel. He might have made some musical plans on these occasions: for example, the addition of the name 'Mr Leigh' (alto) to the score of the 'Caroline' Te Deum (HWV 280).[28] The autograph of the Te Deum shows 'Bayly and Mence' (the altos from the 1749 performance) replaced by 'Leigh' (George Laye?) throughout, and the Chapel opening is the only performance of a Te Deum after 1749 with which Handel was directly concerned that I have been able to trace. No such markings are to be found on the score of any Jubilate,[29] though the Hospital possesses orchestral and vocal parts of the 'Chandos' Jubilate (HWV 246) along with parts for the Foundling Hospital Anthem which may have some connection with the 1753 service.[30] It is almost certain that the principal anthem performed at the Chapel opening was the Foundling Hospital Anthem, and the question arises as to whether Handel subjected the anthem to some revision. The 1749 and 1753 performances were the only ones that Handel gave of this work, though it was also performed in 1759, soon after his death, by J.C. Smith junior as part of a programme of sacred music in memory of Handel.[31] The version given in 1759 is the one which is now found in the original conducting score of the anthem, copied by J.C. Smith senior and including amendments by Handel.[32]

However, the conducting score is made up from two types of paper, and has clearly been added to; moreover, the sections of the anthem in Handel's autograph, now found in the main collection of his autographs at the British Library, are written on different papers and it is clear that he did not originally write the anthem in the form that is found in the final state of the score. The evidence of the major sources from Handel's lifetime is summarised in the table.[33] It seems probable that the version given in the 1749 word-book was a shorter, fully choral, version that did not include the movement 'The people will tell of their wisdom', which a direction on the autograph (R.M. 20.f.12, f. 31v) also excludes. The anthem was preceded in 1749 by a concerto, which presumably also functioned as an opening sinfonia; Smith's copy of the first chorus in the conducting score is headed 'Part 3', indicating quite clearly that the opening aria to the same words was not part of the original score. The first version of the anthem consisted of Nos 2, 3, 3A, 5, 6 and 8. Later, finding that he had Guadagni available, Handel re-set the text of No. 3A as an aria (No. 4), and the conducting score shows that he at one stage toyed with the alternative schemes of putting this movement between Nos 5 and 6 and between Nos 6 and 8. It was perhaps for the latter experiment that the aria in the score carries a direction in Smith's hand for the transposition of the aria up to G major: although this direction is not cancelled, it cannot have been Handel's intention, since the short ending of No. 3B was newly composed to lead into the aria No. 4 in the key of E-flat. The end of No. 3 in the conducting score is clearly a later replacement (presumably for No. 3A, now removed); the other added movements are the duet No. 7 and the opening tenor aria for Thomas Lowe.[34] No. 5 in the score carries Handel's amendments altering the original section for chorus treble and bass in bars 47-63, derived from the Funeral Anthem, into a duet for two solo trebles. It is noteworthy that his handwriting does not occur on the pages that appear to be later insertions to the conducting score.

As we saw above, the 1749 word-book was produced within ten days of the performance. Although Handel would have been able to amend the anthem in this time, it is also possible that the second version of the anthem was prepared on one of the occasions when Handel was approached about the opening of the Chapel. The conducting score is the only evidence that Guadagni might have performed in 1749, but the soloists indicated – Guadagni, Lowe and two trebles – could equally refer to plans made in succeeding years. The music of the rest of the 1749 programme suggests that no fewer than three other alto soloists (Bayly, Mence and Signora Galli) were in action on the same occasion. Comparison of Guadagni's aria 'O God, who from the suckling's mouth' with the musically-related movement 'Happy Iphis' in *Jephtha*, composed in June or July 1751, strongly suggests that the oratorio aria was composed first;[35] in that case it seems most likely that Guadagni did not sing for Handel before 1750, and that Handel's final version of the anthem as found in the conducting score dates from the summer of 1751.

The musical contents of other contemporary sources for the anthem are also shown in the table. The tenor part, written by copyist S6 in the 'original' form, has been amended and added to by Smith senior to give the later version of the anthem: over the added tenor aria No. 1 only the name 'Mr Beard' appears,[36] while above No. 2 the headings '3d Part' and 'Mr. Lowe' have been crossed out and Beard's name has been added, though this too has been cancelled by smudging. The organ part has been included because, although not written by a copyist from the Handel/Smith circle, it is written on paper of a type that was in common use around 1750.[37] It is a fully written keyboard score and may have been prepared for an inexperienced organist. The first movement is headed with Beard's name and No. 4 appears in G major, suggesting the work of an unthinking copyist working from the Foundling Hospital copy. The part-books of the anthem from the Foundling Hospital archives, which were probably written in Handel's lifetime and are entitled 'Anthem … performed before the Prince and Princess of Wales', contain the standard 'final' version of the Anthem.[38]

Anthem for the Foundling Hospital, conducting score copied by J.C. Smith with amendments by Handel © Coram in the care of the Foundling Museum

Apart from being one of the factors delaying the opening of the Chapel, Handel's blindness also naturally made the Governors of the Hospital a little anxious about the future of the profitable *Messiah* performances, and this anxiety had two important consequences. The first concerned the possession of the music itself, over which a famous misunderstanding occurred. In 1754 the Hospital prepared a petition to Parliament for the ownership of rights over *Messiah*,[39] but then discovered that this did not match Handel's intentions. The record of the first stage in the affair adds some illuminating details:

> This Committee being informed by the Treasurer of Mr Handel's kind intention to this Charity, of securing his Oratorio of Messiah to the Hospital, and that it should be performed nowhere else, excepting for his own Benefit: and the Treasurer also acquainting them that he had

been informed by Mr. Handel, That a Copy had been procured from Ireland, with an Intention that ye same should be performed for the Benefit of other Persons

Resolved

That a letter be wrote to Mr. Handel in the Name of this Committee, to return him Thanks for his kind Intention to this Charity; and to assure him, that they will join with him in such Measures as he shall think most proper to secure to the Charity his very valuable benefaction and to prevent his property from being unjustly invaded by any Person whatsoever.

And this Committee are of Opinion That an Act of Parliament should be applied for, to secure this Benefaction of Mr. Handel's, or any other of the like nature, to the sole use & Benefit of this Hospital.[40]

One can well understand how Handel, a man used to leading an active life, became depressed and anxious as he lost his sight. He probably feared that he would no longer be able to control performances of his music, especially if unauthorised manuscript copies circulated. His music was a 'property' on which

a significant part of his income depended, so it is little wonder that he over-reacted when the idea of his music 'going to the Parliament' was presented to him. Fortunately, the affair did not poison his relations with the Hospital, and four months later he agreed to the annual *Messiah* performance; however, the disturbance may have affected the publication of *Messiah*. The circumstances of the first publication of *Songs in Messiah* remain obscure,[41] but supposing that, as suggested earlier, Walsh and Handel shared a common interest in the Hospital,

Ticket for performance of Messiah at the Foundling Hospital, 6 April 1773.

a reasonable hypothesis may be advanced. William C. Smith has dated the preparation of the *Songs* to around the year 1749, based largely on the state of the title page.[42] However, the music pages of Smith's issue 1 are not representative of the plates in their original state, since the later (post-1760) form of the sharp has been added to the basso continuo figurings. Walsh clearly prepared the plates at some time around 1750, but he apparently did not issue prints from them at once and kept them in stock instead. The title page was a different matter: the same plate was used for many oratorio publications with the name of the individual work added from a separate smaller plate, so Walsh probably printed off some title pages for *Songs in Messiah* at once because the plate would have been needed elsewhere. It seems unlikely that Walsh prepared the music plates in 1749, as the single *Messiah* performance of that year (at the Theatre Royal, Covent Garden) does not seem to have been particularly popular. After the resounding success of the Foundling Hospital performances in 1750, by contrast, the oratorio suddenly became much more of a commercial proposition. Having examined copies of most of the oratorio publications with title pages from this plate, I believe that the relevant date may be even later: the title pages that seem close to the condition of *Messiah* 1 are *Esther* 5 and *Jephtha* 2, dating from the period 1751-3.[43] By the time Walsh had prepared the plates he might have heard rumours that Handel intended to give the Hospital rights over the work; after the misunderstanding with the Hospital in January 1754 *Messiah* would have been a sensitive subject, so that it may have seemed better to delay publication until after Handel's death. He did not make provision for the Foundling Hospital to have a copy of the work until the codicil of his will in August 1757.[44] I have not been able to trace a pirated performance in 1753-4 that might have been the start of all the trouble.

The second consequence of Handel's blindness for the Hospital was that it made them return with renewed vigour to the matter of appointing an organist, preferably on Handel's recommendation so that the continuity of the *Messiah* performances could be preserved. Hence, at the same time as thanks for assistance at the Chapel opening were given to Handel, Boyce and Smith, the Sub-committee resolved:

> That the Secretary do apply to Mr. Handel, in order for his direction about having the Organ performed on every Sunday, it being the Request of several Ladies of distinction.[45]

It is clear from the minutes of the committee meetings of June 1754 that the appointment of J.C. Smith junior as organist was influenced by the need to continue the *Messiah* performances;[46] indeed, although some distant responsibility for the weekly running of the Chapel's music may have been involved, the only duty explicitly given to the organist in the minutes during Handel's lifetime was stated when Handel approved the appointment of 'Mr Smith Organist to the Chapel to conduct his Musical Compositions'. Smith was appointed later in the year, the Hospital having in the meantime found a solution to the problem of providing a permanent salary for the post by successfully petitioning the Crown for a grant to cover the routine Chapel expenses. When the vocal and instrumental parts of *Messiah* were prepared for the Hospital in 1759 in accordance with the instructions in Handel's will, the copies were derived from a set of parts used for performances in 1754. There is a strong probability that the latter were prepared for Smith's use when control of the performances effectively passed from the composer's hands, and that they were brought out again for use in each subsequent year.[47] It is no accident that the first surviving expense account for the Foundling Hospital *Messiah* performances dates from 1754: this was the first occasion on which Handel was only indirectly involved, and for that reason the Secretary was careful to copy all the details into the minutes. Nevertheless, it is clear that the handover to Smith made very little difference to the performances themselves: from 1750 at least, Smith senior had been in charge of organising the performers,[48] and the minutes, mainly routine for the later years, show that Handel was consulted through Smith junior over the dates and arrangements. Handel is sometimes thanked as if he were still in charge, but his role in the later performances was little more than that of a figurehead. Since the minutes rarely describe the person concerned as anything other than 'Mr. Smith', it is occasionally difficult to discover whether father or son is intended, though all the references before the Chapel opening in 1753 seem to refer to Smith senior and in general there is a clear demarcation between the musical functions of the younger Smith and the business arrangements handled by his father.[49]

With such provision for the smooth running of the *Messiah* performances, it is not surprising that they successfully survived the death of the composer, and also that of Smith senior in 1763, by which time the Sub-committee was referring to them as the 'Annual Musical Festival of Messiah'.[50] The business arrangements for the

A list of performers and singers at the performance of Messiah at the Foundling Hospital Chapel on Friday 2 May 1760 © Coram in the care of the Foundling Museum

performances passed into the hands of William Teede, the elder Smith's son-in-law, and the surviving expense account from the 1763 performance (the first one after Smith senior's death) is illuminating on two points. First Teede himself, in addition to being paid as an oboe player, received at the end of the account an additional five guineas, presumably for arranging the performance and providing the music; this indicates that parallel payments to 'Smith' in earlier accounts refer to the elder Smith, and are not payments to his son as organist. Secondly the account, written in the hand of S5, is signed by Teede himself with a hand sufficiently characteristic to identify him as the copyist hitherto designated S6

– the copyist of most of the Foundling Hospital Anthem tenor part, and the one who in the main shared with Smith senior the task of copying out the score and parts of *Messiah* provided for the Hospital by Handel's will.[51] Teede and Smith junior continued the performances, to rather thinner audiences than Handel had attracted, until 1769, when the Committee made a diplomatic blunder by approaching Giardini to arrange the *Messiah* performance for the opening of the Parker organ that replaced the one Handel had presented. Having learned of the performance through an advertisement in the newspapers, Smith protested to the Committee that

> in regard to the appointment of several Persons to be Performers by Mr. Giardini, as well as past transactions between them, it would by no means be agreeable for him to mix in the said Performance.[52]

One result of Smith's withdrawal was that the Hospital authorities had, for the first time, to make their own arrangements for the hire of the Chapel Royal boys. Although another performance under Smith's management was talked of, nothing came of it and Smith resigned his post at the Hospital. There followed a few performances under various managements, with John Stanley providing some continuity. After the 1772 performance had realised a profit of only £14.10s.0d. to the Hospital, the Linleys were engaged as a special attraction, which succeeded in bringing the audience back again the next year. Nevertheless, the performances in the 1770s gradually lost impetus and finally foundered in 1778 because one of the soloists was not available on a suitable date. One cannot imagine that such an event would have prevented the performance under the management of Handel or Smith. However, this misfortune ended the run of nearly 30 years of Handel performances which had begun with the composer's new interest in 1749, and which had absorbed a considerable amount of his energies in the years 1749-53.

Text © the author; this is a revised version of an article originally published in *Music & Letters*, July 1977.

TABLE
Variants of the Founding Hospital Anthem found in the Sources

Movement	1749 Wordbook	Autograph	FH Score (Smith copy): paper type*	Tenor Part (RCM 2254) & copyist	Organ Part (RCM 2273)	FH Parts vol. 135	1759 Wordbook
1 Blessed are they (Tenor aria)	–	–	Y	Smith (addition)	+	+	
2 Blessed are they (Chorus)	Chorus	–	X	S6	+	+	Aria & Chorus
3 They deliver the poor (Chorus)	Chorus & Verse	R.M.20.d.9, marked for re-use	X	S6	+	+	Chorus
3A O God, who from the suckling's mouth (Chorus)	Verse & Chorus	R.M.20.f.12, Paper A	(removed)	S6 deleted later	–	–	–
3B Shortened ending to No. 3		–	Y	added	+	+	
4 O God, who from the suckling's mouth (Aria)	–	R.M.20.f.12, Paper B	Y	'Aria tacet' added by Smith	+†	+	Aria
5 The Charitable shall be had in everlasting remembrance (Chorus)	Verse & Chorus	R.M.20.d.9, marked for re-use	X	S6	+	+	Duetto & Chorus
6 Comfort them - Keep them alive (Chorus)	Verse & Chorus	R.M.20.f.12 removed from Susanna, with addition ff. 24-25	X	S6	+	+	Chorus - Chorus
7 The people will tell (Treble duet)	–	R.M.20.f.12, Paper B	Y	'Verse for 2 Boy's' added by Smith	+	+	Accompagnament & Duetto
8 Hallelujah (Chorus)	Full chorus	Cue R.M.20.f.12 f. 31v. Music copied from R.M. 20.f.2	X	S6	+	+	Chorus

* The score was originally written on Paper X (watermark Clausen Co, 10-stave pages ruled with 5-stave rastra, total span 92 mm.); insertions or amendments are on Paper Y (watermark Clausen Cp; 10-stave pages ruled with 5-stave rastra, total span 89.5 mm.)
+ indicates that the named movement is present.
† in G major.

APPENDIX
Attendances at Foundling Hospital Performances
and
Present Location of Performance Expense Accounts

YEAR	DATE	TICKETS		LOCATION OF ACCOUNT
		Sold	complimentary	
1749	May 27	c.700*		
1750	May 1	1,387		
	May 15	599		
1751	April 18	1,218		
	May 16	785	4	
1752	April 9	1,223		
1753	April 16	283	802†	
	May 1	1,063	12	
1754	May 15	1,27		Committee minutes
1755	May 1	1,396	39	
1756	May 19	1,370	35	
1757	May 5	1,070	37	
1758	April 27	814	46	Separate account sheet

Handel died 14 April 1759

YEAR	DATE	TICKETS		LOCATION OF ACCOUNT
1759	May 3	892		Separate account sheet
1760	May 2	541		Separate account sheet
1761	April 24	436		
1762	May 5	217		

Smith senior died January 1763

YEAR	DATE	TICKETS		LOCATION OF ACCOUNT
1763	April 29	293		Separate account sheet
1764	May 8	241		
1765	April 2	233		
1766	April 15	377		
1767	April 29	352		Sub-committee minutes
1768	May 12	318		

End of performances under the direction of J. C. Smith

YEAR	DATE	TICKETS		LOCATION OF ACCOUNT
1769	November 29	431		Sub-committee minutes
1770	April 12			
1771	April 30	387	51	Committee minutes
1772	May 7	184		Committee minutes
1773	April 6	874		Committee minutes
1774	March 29	788	70	Committee minutes
1775	November 23	308	53	Committee minutes
1776	April 2	263		
1777	May 9	299	56	Sub-committee minutes

Tickets sold are calculated from receipts given in the Hospital records, on the basis of half a guinea per ticket. On some occasions generous supporters of the Hospital undoubtedly bought more tickets than they used. The issue of complimentary tickets is only sporadically recorded in the minutes: it seems to have been done on a fairly casual basis in the early years and was not treated in detail in the minutes for Messiah performances until control had passed out of Handel's hands (1755: S, ii. 19). The size of the audience dropped abruptly in 1760, the year after Handel's death, in spite of the presence of Princess Amelia at the performance.
Apart from the mixed concert on 27 May 1749 and the opening of the Chapel on 16 April 1753, all performances are of *Messiah*.

* Figure based on the income of £351. 3s. 0d. recorded in the table of donations (C iii, p. 328, 27 May 1752). This may be a mistake for £381. 3s. 0d. (726 tickets) or may be a net figure after the deduction of expenses. Handel was given £50 to distribute 'in such a manner as he shall think fit' (C iii, p. 19).
† The Sub-committee (S i, p. 163), considering the arrangements for the Chapel opening, recommended the disposal of 802 of the 1,200 available tickets to Governors & c., but it is not clear whether these are to be the 'Gratis Tickets' referred to elsewhere in the minute. Only 800 tickets were put on sale to the public (S i, p. 180; Deutsch, Handel, pp. 738-9).

[1] There are three series of Minute Books: General Court (G), General Committee (C) and Sub-Committee (S), all now held at the London Metropolitan Archive. References in this article supplement those in Otto Erich Deutsch, *Handel: A Documentary Biography* (London, 1955), which were mainly drawn from the published histories of the Hospital by John Brownlow (1847, 1858, 1881) and R. H. Nichols & F. A. Wray (1935), and the article by F. G. E[dwards] in *The Musical Times*, May-June 1902. A new, more comprehensive, collection of Handel Documents is currently in preparation.

[2] G i, p. 181.

[3] Deutsch, *Handel*, p. 669 (misdated 7 May). This meeting was unusual for being held on a Thursday, perhaps to accommodate Handel: the Committee usually met on Wednesdays.

[4] 10 May: C iii, p. 9, G i, p. 194; 24 May: S I, p. 33.

[5] See Donald J. Burrows, 'Handel's Peace Anthem', *The Musical Times*, cxiv (1973), pp. 1230-32, also (for HWV 266 and 268) Donald Burrows, *Handel and the English Chapel Royal* (Oxford, 2005), chapters 14-15.

[6] See Winton Dean, *Handel's Dramatic Oratorios and Masques* (London, 1959), p. 526.

[7] Hamburg, Staats-und Universitätsbibliothek, M C/268, f. 143v.

[8] The proceeds of this concert were not recorded in the minutes at the time. See the notes to the Appendix.

[9] C iii, p.17.

[10] C iii, p. 90; partly quoted in Deutsch, *Handel*, p. 679.

[11] S i, p. 57.

[12] C iii, p. 93.

[13] 7 March: C iii, p. 99.

[14] See the comment in George Harris's diary for 15 May 1750, in Donald Burrows and Rosemary Dunhill, *Music and Theatre in Handel's World* (Oxford, 2002), p.271, and Donald Burrows, *Organs and organists at the Foundling Hospital, 1750-1800* http://www.music.ed.ac.uk/russell/conference/Burrowsonorganists.html

[15] Details are given in S i, p. 60 (25 April).

[16] C iii, pp. 169-71.

[17] See Deutsch, *Handel*, pp. 692, 710. Payments recorded for performers', servants', and constables' expenses in 1750 and 1751 are confusing and probably incomplete: see the summary table in Donald Burrows, 'Handel's Performances of "Messiah": the Evidence of the Conducting Score', *Music & Letters*, lvi (1975), p. 334, which is based on all available records. It is clear, however, that payments to Gates cover two performances (pace John Tobin, '"Messiah" Restored - An Apologia', *The Musical Times*, xci (1950), p. 133).

[18] S i, p. 188, where Gates is thanked for the boys' performance on 1 May 1753. A marginal note says 'a mistake'.

[19] S i, p. 90.

[20] C iii, p. 256.

✥

[21] C iv, p. 37; partly quoted in Deutsch, *Handel*, p. 726.

[22] C iv, p.. 49. For the subsequent resolutions see Deutsch, *Handel*, p. 728.

[23] 13 December 1752: S i, p. 163. See the note to the Appendix.

[24] G i, p. 259. I have found no evidence that the rehearsal of the music planned for 25 January (Deutsch, *Handel*, p. 731) took place. Isaac Maddox, Bishop of Worcester, was one of the few bishops of the period to preach before the Sons of the Clergy (E. H. Pearce, *The Sons of the Clergy*, London, 1929, p. 250); his Foundling Hospital sermon, 'The Wisdom and Duty of Preserving Destitute Infants', still retains an air of conviction.

[25] S i, p. 180. See Deutsch, *Handel*, p. 739.

[26] C iv, p. 78; Deutsch, *Handel*, p. 740.

[27] *London Evening Post*, 3-5 April 1753; not in Deutsch, *Handel*.

[28] British Library RM 20.g.4, f. 38.

[29] The original newspaper advertisement for the Chapel opening mentions a Jubilate, but none is referred to in the reports of the service published in the newspapers dated 14-17 April.

[30] Vol. 135. The parts for the Foundling Hospital Anthem and the Jubilate are in the same hand, the former having B and C (possibly Clausen's Cp) type watermarks and the latter combining a shield (sinister)/GR mark with the countermark IV. This watermark is not listed in Hans Dieter Clausen, *Händels Direktionspartituren* (Hamburg, 1973), but it is probably a transitional watermark from some time during the 1750s. Bound with these are parts (approximately contemporary) for the Cannons Anthem *O sing unto the Lord* (HWV 246) in the hands of two other scribes.

[31] Word-book for the 1759 performance in Paris, Bibliothèque Nationale, Schoelcher Collection; another copy, incomplete but giving the complete Anthem text, British Library, 10747.f.13.(2.). An attempt was made to secure the Chapel Royal boys for a performance of some anthem at the Hospital's charity sermon just after Christmas 1753 (S, i, p. 206), but apparently nothing came of it. There is no evidence for a performance in 1750, mentioned by Chrysander in the preface to vol. 36 of the *Händel-Gesellschaft* edition (1872).

[32] This is the version printed, with one variant, in *HG* xxxvi, p. 154. The conducting score of the Foundling Hospital Anthem is now at the Foundling Museum. For a modern edition of the anthem, see George Frideric Handel, ed. Donald Burrows, *Foundling Hospital Anthem* (London, 1983; full score with critical commentary).

[33] The version of the anthem found in Royal College of Music MS 245, which combines sections of the Foundling Hospital Anthem with movements derived from other Handel anthems and a recitative and aria adapted from *Giulio Cesare*, has been ignored: there is no evidence that it reflects any performance that had Handel's authority.

[34] The aria, for which no autograph can be found, looks like the revision of an earlier (Italian?) aria; a copying error by Smith in the conducting score appears to support this hypothesis. In Lcm MS 2254 Smith has altered the words of the aria (but not the chorus) to 'Blessed is he that considereth ...'.

[35] This would rule out any possibility that Handel revised the anthem for Thomas Coram's

funeral in the Foundling Hospital Chapel on 3 April 1751. That occasion had a 'choir service', but without orchestra, and without any involvement by Handel.

[36] Watermark Clausen Cp, which supports a dating after 1749 for this addition.

[37] Watermark Clausen Cm.

[38] See note 30.

[39] The full text of the petition (partly printed in Deutsch, *Handel*, pp. 756-7) is found in C iv, p. 145.

[40] S i, p. 211 (2 January 1754).

[41] See Watkins Shaw, *A Textual and Historical Companion to Handel's Messiah* (London, 1965), pp. 129-31, and W. C. Smith, *Concerning Handel* (London, 1948), chapter III, esp. pp. 102-8.

[42] *Handel: a Descriptive Catalogue of the Early Editions* (2nd edn, Oxford, 1970), pp. 116-17. All references to the printed editions of the oratorios are to the numbers in this catalogue.

[43] Smith, *A Descriptive Catalogue*, p. 109. *Jephtha 2* is presumably the new edition of February 1753 (p. 334).

[44] It is probably significant that Walsh's successors were unable to produce any contract relating to the publication of *Messiah* when this was required in a subsequent court case: see Ronald J. Rabin and Stephen Zohn, 'Arne, Handel, Walsh and Music as Intellectual Property', *Journal of the Royal Musical Association* cxx/1 (1995), pp. 112-145.

[45] S i, p. 185 (18 April 1753.)

[46] C iv, pp. 181, 187; Deutsch, *Handel*, pp. 752-3.

[47] Analysis of the casts involved and the singers' names on the conducting score of *Messiah* suggests that the 1754 performance was a repeat of the version given by Handel in the previous year, except that the alto part was divided to provide for an additional soprano soloist, after the necessary transposition. The same version of *Messiah* was therefore available to Smith in a form which could be used with four soloists or five.

[48] See the receipt transcribed in *The Musical Times*, May 1902, p. 306.

[49] On one occasion both Smiths make a brief appearance in the same minute: on 31 March 1761 (C vii, p. 418), as 'Mr. Smith the Organist was in the Country for his Health', 'Mr. Smith the Father' attended the Committee meeting to arrange the *Messiah* performance date.

[50] S iv, p. 143.

[51] For copyists S5 and S6, see Jens Peter Larsen, *Handel's 'Messiah': Origins, Composition, Sources* (London, 1955), chapter 4.

[52] C xii, p. 182.

4

Catalogue

1. (Cover) George Frideric Handel
Oil on canvas by Thomas Hudson (1701-1779)

Showing the composer in old age and blind this monumental portrait was executed for Charles Jennens. The open book in front of the composer is inscribed "Messiah" which also appeared in Hudson's earlier portrait of Handel. This painting was the subject of the National Portrait Gallery's first national appeal.

Loaned by the National Portrait Gallery, London

❖

2. Portrait of Handel in the style of Francis van der Myn
Oil on canvas; late eighteenth century

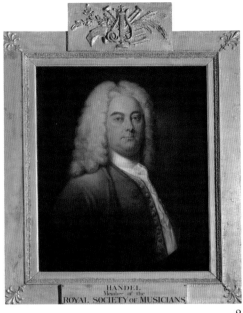

This portrait appears to be an exact copy of another in the Society's collection; that portrait may well have been owned by Matthew Dubourg (1703-1767) who led the orchestra in the first performance of Messiah (Dublin, 13 April 1742) and whose son-in-law, Redmond Simpson (ca. 1730-1783), gave it to the Society. Simpson performed in the Foundling Hospital Messiah performance of 1754.

2

Loaned by the Royal Society of Musicians of Great Britain

The Minutes of the last Meeting were read and approved
Mr. Handel being present & having Generously and
Charitably offered a Performance of Vocal & Instrumental
Musick to be at this Hospital, and that the Money arising
therefrom should be applied to the finishing the Chapel of
the Hospital.

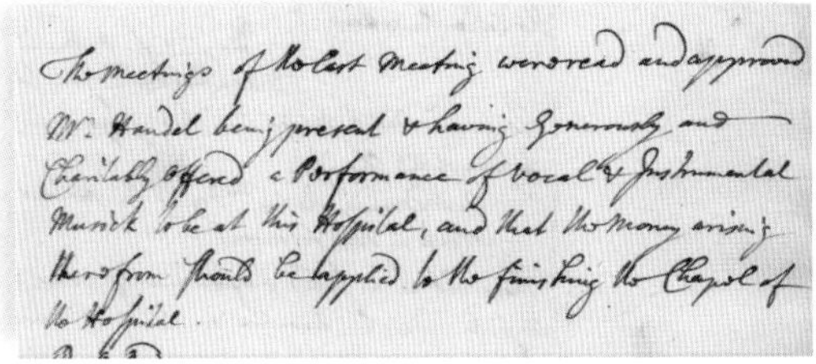

3 *detail*

3. Minutes of the Foundling Hospital General Committee
Facsimile of the meeting of 4 May 1749

Handel attended this meeting to offer the charity a benefit performance.

Reproduced by permission of Coram

5

4. (See page 29) The Foundling Hospital / L'Hospital des Enfants Trouvés
Coloured engraving; ca. 1775

Printed for R. Wilkinson and Bowles and Carver.

Gerald Coke Handel Collection, accession no. 5214

5. The Chapel, Foundling Hospital
Steel engraving with aquatint by John Bluck; 1808

Published by R. Ackermann.

Gerald Coke Handel Collection, accession no. 5219

✥

6

6a

7a

7

6. Blessed are they that consider the poor, the Foundling Hospital Anthem
Autograph score; 1749

Handel composed this anthem for a concert to mark the opening of the Chapel at the Foundling Hospital. His conducting score from that performance is displayed in the museum's ground floor gallery.

7. Foundling Hospital Anthem
Manuscript copy; late eighteenth century

This manuscript differs from other versions in certain movements; it includes a movement from Giulio Cesare.

8. A Performance of Musick, For the Benefit of the Hospital for the Maintenance and Education of Exposed and Deserted Young Children, on Thursday the 25th of May, 1749

The concert included the first performance of Handel's Foundling Hospital Anthem; to accommodate the presence of the Prince and Princess of Wales the performance was delayed until Saturday 27, although this programme book had already been sent to the printer.

By permission of the Provost and Scholars of King's College, Cambridge (Rowe Music Library, Mn.20.49.)

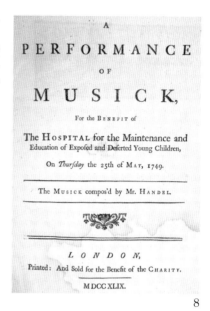

8

9. George Frederick Handel

Watercolour on ivory by Georg Andreas Wolffgang (1703-1745) Probably painted ca. 1737-9.

Loaned by Her Majesty the Queen Royal Collection © 2009 Her Majesty Queen Elizabeth II

9

10

10. Declaration of Trust: The Society of Musicians
Ink on parchment; 28 August 1739

The Society was established at its first meeting on Sunday 23 April 1738 and on 7 May the Rules of the Society were first printed. No copy of these Rules survives but it is unlikely that they were substantially different when this Indenture was drawn up the following year. There are 228 Members listed in the document.

Loaned by the Royal Society of Musicians of Great Britain

> To the Governors of the Society for the Support of decayed
> Musicians and their Families.
>
> GENTLEMEN,
>
> WE whose Names are hereunto subscribed, beg Leave to recommend
> *Mr William Teede*
> a Member of this Society for immediate Relief from this Charity, He
> *is a Widower, but by Age, and the Infirmity*
> *of Lameness in both Hands is render'd incapable*
> *of providing for himself the Necessaries of Subsistance*
> *therefore begs the Assistance of this Society.* ——

11 *detail*

11. Petition of relief for William Teede
5 October, 1777

This document is one of the earliest extant appeals to the Society of Musicians and comes from the widower William Teede who had worked as one of Handel's copyists as well as playing the oboe in the Foundling Hospital *Messiah* performances of 1754 and 1758. "But by Age, and the Infirmity of Lameness on both hands [he] is render'd incapable of providing for Himself the Necessaries of Subsistence therefore begs the Assistance of this Society".

Loaned by the Royal Society of Musicians of Great Britain

12

12. George Frideric Handel
Line engraving by Jacobus Houbraken; 1738

Portrait of Handel within an ornamental frame with a scene from *Alexander's Feast*. First produced for the subscribers to the printed score of *Alexander's Feast* this print was used as a frontispiece to many later published scores.

Gerald Coke Handel Collection, accession no. 5207

✤

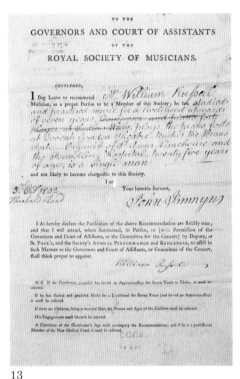

13

13. Royal Society of Musicians application form
1802-3

William Russell's application for membership.

Loaned by the Royal Society of Musicians of Great Britain

14. Alexander's Feast
Autograph score; 1735-36

Alexander's Feast, although first performed in 1736, was revived for the first concert in aid of the Society of Musicians; it was directed by Handel and the monies raised were entirely "For the benefit and Increase of a Fund established for the support of Decay'd Musicians and their Families". Handel also gave the theatre for the evening and the impresario John James Heidegger gave £20 to defray other expenses incurred by the Society.

Loaned by the British Library Board; R.M.20.d.4.

14a

14

❖

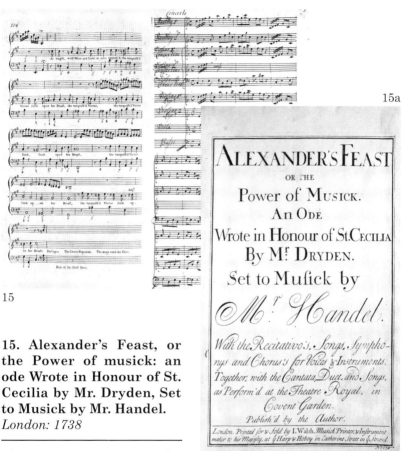

15a

15

15. Alexander's Feast, or the Power of musick: an ode Wrote in Honour of St. Cecilia by Mr. Dryden, Set to Musick by Mr. Handel.
London: 1738

The 1739 word-book for *Alexander's Feast* mentions the insertion of various concertos within the performance; in this printed volume the manuscripts have been sewn in those exact places. It is most likely that this volume was used for one of the performances of the work in 1739, which were all directed by Handel, when he also played the two organ concertos. The beginning of the concerto grosso (known as "Concerto in Alexander's Feast") is shown here at the end of the first part.

Gerald Coke Handel Collection, accession nos 2542 and 2543

16. Alexander's Feast; or, the Power of Musick: an Ode Wrote in Honour of St. Cecilia ... by Mr. Dryden

London: printed for J. and R. Tonson, 1739

Word-book for use at performances and probably used at the benefit concert for the Society of Musicians at King's Theatre on 20 March.

Gerald Coke Handel Collection, accession no. 5

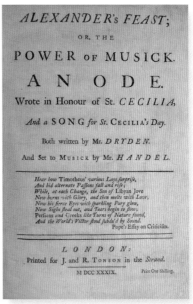

16

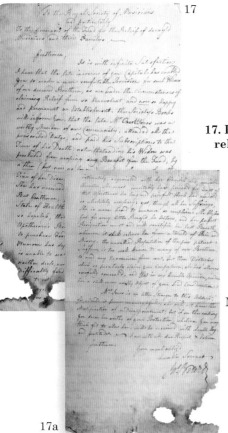

17

17. Letter by John Beard requesting relief for Mrs Esther Jones, widow of Charles Jones

[London]: 1784?

Esther Jones (née Young) married Charles Jones (d. 1780) in about 1762. She performed for many years at Covent Garden and had a considerable stage career. On the death of her husband a benefit performance was held for her on 18 May 1780 and it is probable that she was no longer performing.

Loaned by the Royal Society of Musicians of Great Britain

17a

❖

18

18. John Beard by Thomas Hudson
Oil on canvas; ca. 1743

John Beard sang in many of the first and early performances of Handel's oratorios.

Gerald Coke Handel Collection, accession no. 5201

❖

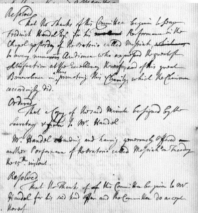

19 detail

19. Minutes of the Foundling Hospital General Committee
Facsimile of the meeting of 2 May 1750

The committee thanks Handel for the performance of *Messiah* on the previous day. Too many tickets were sold and a second performance was hastily arranged.

Reproduced by permission of Coram

19a detail

20. Gustavus Waltz
Oil on canvas by J.M. Hauck; ca. 1755

Gustavus Waltz (fl. 1732-1759) sang bass in Handel's operas from 1733-1736 and thereafter in many of the oratorios. He is listed among the singers in the Foundling Hospital *Messiah* performances of 1754, 1758 and 1759. Both the music historians Charles Burney and John Hawkins note the singer as having been Handel's cook although there is no other evidence for this; he is depicted here with refreshments in the background.

Gerald Coke Handel Collection, accession no. 5212

21

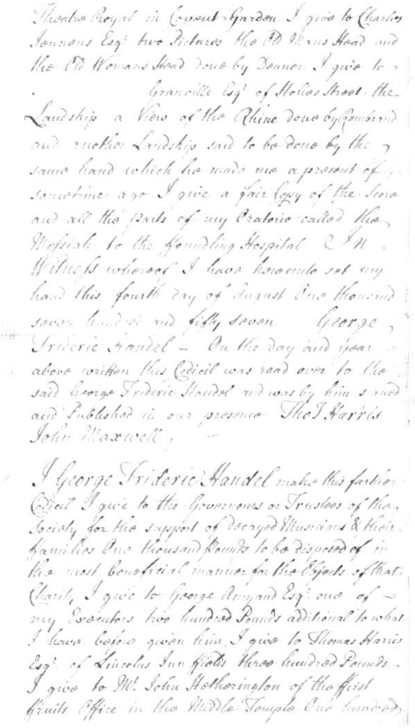

Theatre Royal in Covent Garden. I give to Charles Jennens Esq. two Pictures the Old Mans Head and the Old Womans Head done by Denner. I give to Granville Esq. of Holles Street the Landship a View of the Rhine done by Rembrand and another Landship said to be done by the same hand which he made me a present of sometime ago. I give a fair Copy of the Score and all the Parts of my Oratorio called the Messiah to the Foundling Hospital. In Witness whereof I have hereunto set my hand this fourth day of August One thousand seven hundred and fifty seven. George Frideric Handel. On the day and year above written this Codicil was read over to the said George Frideric Handel and was by him signed and Published in our presence Tho. Harris John Maxwell.

I George Frideric Handel make this farther Codicil I give to the Governours or Trustees of the Society for the support of decayed Musicians & their Families One thousand Pounds to be disposed of in the most beneficial manner for the Objects of that Charity. I give to George Amyand Esq. one of my Executors two hundred Pounds additional to what I have before given him. I give to Thomas Harris Esq. of Lincolns Inn fields three hundred Pounds. I give to Mr. John Hetherington of the first fruits Office in the Middle Temple One hundred

21. Executor's copy of Handel's will
London; 1759

The left-hand page shows benefactions to both the Foundling Hospital and the Society of Musicians. The composer's own copy of his will and codicils is displayed in the permanent exhibition on the second floor.

Loaned by The Royal College of Music (from the collection of the Sacred Harmonic Society), MS 2190 ff. 2v-3r

22

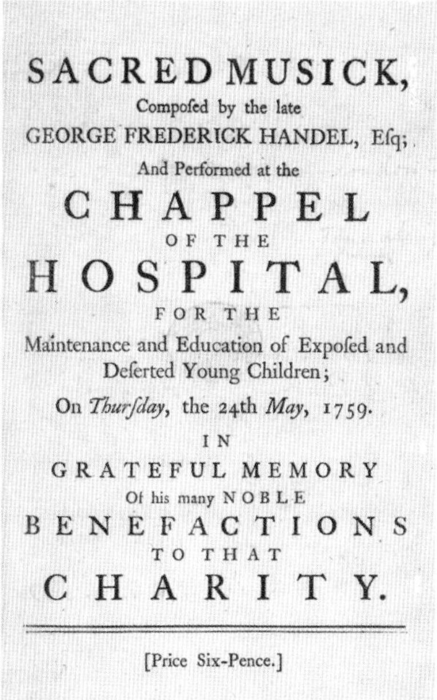

SACRED MUSICK,
Composed by the late
GEORGE FREDERICK HANDEL, Esq;
And Performed at the
CHAPPEL
OF THE
HOSPITAL,
FOR THE
Maintenance and Education of Exposed and Deserted Young Children;
On *Thursday*, the 24th *May*, 1759.
IN
GRATEFUL MEMORY
Of his many NOBLE
BENEFACTIONS
TO THAT
CHARITY.
[Price Six-Pence.]

22. Sacred Musick, Composed by the late George Frederick Handel Esq., and performed at the Chappel of the Hospital for the Maintenance and Education of Exposed and Deserted Young Children
[London]: 24 May 1759

Programme book of the concert at the Foundling Hospital shortly after the composer's death on 14 April.

Loaned by the British Library Board; 10347.f.13.(2.)

23

23. Messiah, an Oratorio: Tenor Principale
Manuscript vocal part; 1760

From the set of performance parts bequeathed by Handel to the Foundling Hospital. With the name of the celebrated tenor singer John Beard ("Mr Beard") and possibly used by him in performance.

Loaned by Coram

24. A list of performers and singers at the performance of Messiah at the Foundling Hospital Chapel on Friday 2 May 1760

John Beard gave his services for free and the Master of the "6 Boys" from the Chapel Royal was later to return their payment less travel expenses incurred; John Christopher Smith received all monies and disbursed payments to individuals. The orchestral musicians are listed on the recto.

Loaned by Coram

24

25

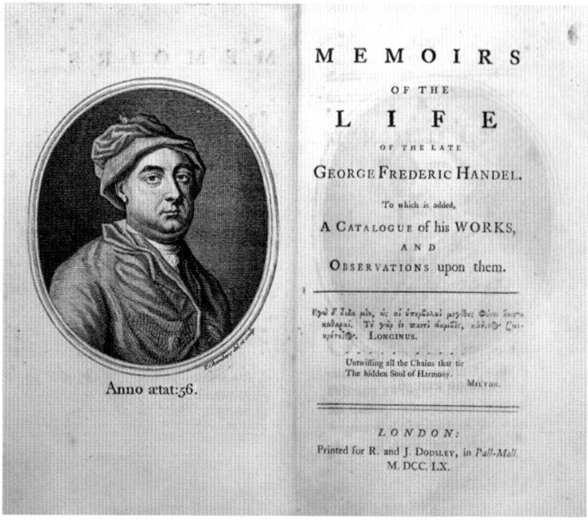

25. Memoirs of the life of the late George Frederic Handel, to which is added a catalogue of his works and observations upon them [by John Mainwaring]
London: R. and J. Dodsley, 1760

M E M O I R S
OF THE
L I F E
OF THE LATE
GEORGE FREDERIC HANDEL.
To which is added,
A CATALOGUE of his WORKS,
AND
OBSERVATIONS upon them.

Anno ætat:56.

LONDON:
Printed for R. and J. DODSLEY, in *Pall-Mall.*
M. DCC. LX.

John Mainwaring (1735-1807) produced the first extended biography of any European composer. The author obtained much of the biographical information from John Christopher Smith. The frontispiece portrait is by Thomas Chambars (1724-1789).

Gerald Coke Handel Collection, accession no. 348

26. Gold medal struck on the occasion of the Commemoration Concerts of 1784
London; 1784

A medal was given to each of the 525 performers.

Loaned by the Royal Society of Musicians of Great Britain

26

✤

AT a General Meeting of the ROYAL SOCIETY of MUSICIANS, held at the Feathers Tavern in the Strand, the 25th day of June 1786, when Eighty-one Members were prefent, Mr. REDMOND SIMPSON in the Chair, The Chairman propofed the following refolutions; he having previoufly informed them, that he had received from the Earl of Sandwich, Honorary Prefident, the Moft Honourable the Marquis of Carmarthen, the Earls of Exeter and Uxbridge, the Right Honourable Lord Vifcount Dudley and Ward, the Right Honourable Lord Vifcount Fitzwilliam, the Right Honourable Lord Grey de Wilton, Sir Watkin Williams Wynn, Bart. Sir Richard Jebb, Bart. and Joah Bates, Efq; Honorary Vice-Prefidents of the Society, and Directors of the Mufical Feftival in Weftminfter Abbey, 3300l. for the ufe of this charity.

Refolved, That the moft humble and grateful thanks of this Society be prefented to the Earl of Sandwich, the Marquis of Carmarthen, the Earls of Exeter and Uxbridge, the Lord Vifcount Dudley and Ward, the Lord Vifcount Fitzwilliam, the Lord Grey de Wilton, Sir Watkin Williams Wynn, Bart. Sir Richard Jebb, Bart. and Joah Bates, Efq; for their great condefcenfion in having undertaken, and their zeal and trouble in managing, the performances at the Mufical Feftival in Weftminfter Abbey this year.

Refolved, That the moft fincere and grateful acknowledgments of this Society be likewife prefented to Joah Bates, Efq; for his having planned and felected the mufic, and conducted a Band, exceeding any ever affembled before in this, or perhaps in any other country, with refpect to its magnitude and the profeffional abilities of its members, in a manner fo fingularly honourable to himfelf, and fo beneficial to the Society.

Refolved, That the moft Honourable the Marquis of Carmarthen be Honorary Prefident; and the Earls of Exeter, Sandwich, and Uxbridge, the Right Honourable Lord Vifcount Dudley and Ward, the Right Honourable Lord Vifcount Fitzwilliam, the Right Honourable Lord Grey de Wilton, Sir Watkin Williams Wynn, Bart. Sir Richard Jebb, Bart. and Joah Bates, Efq; be Honorary Vice-Prefidents for the enfuing year. All which refolutions were unanimoufly agreed to.

REDMOND SIMPSON, Chairman.

27 detail

28. The Morning Chronicle, and London Advertiser, no. 5617
Monday May 14, 1787

Advertisement for the performance on 28 May at Westminster Abbey, one of the concerts of the fourth Grand Musical Festival which raised funds for the Royal Society of Musicians.

Loaned by the Royal Society of Musicians of Great Britain

27. The London Chronicle for 1786, July 11-15

Newspaper account publicly advertising the income of the Handel festival of 1786; £3300 was raised for the charitable fund of the Royal Society of Musicians.

Loaned by the Royal Society of Musicians of Great Britain

28

29. Handel holding a score of Messiah
Oil on canvas, probably by Francis Kyte (fl. 1710-1745); ca. 1743

Gerald Coke Handel Collection, accession no. 5222

29

30

30. The Grand Musical Festival that took place in Westminster Abbey in June 1834
Engraving by William Woolnoth; 1834. Proof state

The fourth performance of this festival included the *Messiah*; the other three concerts included many works by Handel and the funds raised by the concerts were split between the Royal Society of Musicians, the New Musical Fund, the Choral Fund and the Royal Academy of Music.

Loaned by the Royal Society of Musicians of Great Britain

✥

31. Advertisement bill for performance of Messiah for the benefit of the Royal Society of Musicians, June the 5th, 1839

Printed by J. Mallett: 1839

Loaned by the Royal Society of Musicians of Great Britain

31

32. Selection of benefit concert tickets
London, Birmingham: ca. 1775-1834

Luigi Borghi (ca. 1745-ca. 1806) was leader of the second violins at the Handel Commemoration concerts of 1784. Felice Giardini (1716-1796) was a governor at the Foundling Hospital. The Mr Jones may be the husband of Mrs Jones referred to in John Beard's letter (see exhibit no. 17).

Gerald Coke Handel Collection

32 detail

33. W. Cramer
Stipple engraving by Thomas Hardy after his own portrait; 1794
Published by J. Bland

Wilhelm Cramer (1746-1799) was one of the two leaders of the orchestra during the Handel Commemoration concerts of 1784.

Gerald Coke Handel Collection, accession no. 5208

33

34. Mr Ricd Randall
Etching; 1812

Richard Randall (1736-1828) is shown wearing one of the commemoration medals from the 1784 performances; he sang in the festival concerts, was a chorister in the Chapel Royal and sang in Handel's oratorio concerts.

Gerald Coke Handel Collection, accession no. 5220

34

35

35. A musical doctor & his scholars
Coloured caricature by Thomas Rowlandson; ca. 1790

Unattributed but possibly depicting Charles Burney the music historian and writer, organist, composer and teacher who wrote an account of the Handel Commemoration concerts of 1784.

Gerald Coke Handel Collection, accession no. 5225

36. Joseph Hayden

Stipple engraving by Georg Siegmund Facius after the portrait by John Hoppner (1758-1810)
Published by Messrs Facius.

The famous Austrian composer Joseph Haydn (1732-1809) attended a "Grand Music meeting" (the Handel Commemoration concerts at Westminster Abbey) during the final week of May 1791.

Gerald Coke Handel Collection, accession no. 5206

36

37. Mr: Beard

Mezzotint by John Faber jr after the portrait by John Michael Williams.
London: 1749

John Beard sang at the Foundling Hospital in 1749 when this print was published.

Gerald Coke Handel Collection, accession no. 5223

37

38. John Hebden
Mezzotint by John Faber jr after the portrait by Philip Mercier which is now lost; 1741

John Hebden (ca. 1705-1765) played in the orchestra of the Hospital's benefit performances of *Messiah* in 1754 and 1758.

Gerald Coke Handel Collection, accession no. 5202

38

39. John James Heidegger
Mezzotint by John Faber jr after the portrait by Jean Baptiste van Loo;
Sold by Faber, 1749

The impresario Heidegger (1666-1749) worked with Handel for many years, especially during the composer's opera period; he gave money to defray the expenses of the opening concert for the Society of Musicians in 1739.

Gerald Coke Handel Collection, accession no. 5207

39

40. S. Arnold, Organist and Composer to his Majesty
Stipple engraving by Thomas Hardy; 1797
Published by F. Linley

Samuel Arnold (1740-1802) was a philanthropic musician of the eighteenth century: he was a prominent member of the Society of Musicians, conducted annual performances for the benefit of the charity entitled "Sons of the Clergy", as an active mason conducted the Freemasons' concerts in aid of the Asylum for Female Orphans, as well as setting up the Choral Fund in 1791. He edited the first edition of Handel's works.

40

Gerald Coke Handel Collection, accession no. 5205

41

41. George Frederic Handel
Engraved by Francesco Bartolozzi after the drawing by Giovanni Battista Cipriani; ca. 1790

Medallion portrait of Handel, with angels, used as one of several frontispieces to Dr Samuel Arnold's collected "complete" edition [1787-1797]. The composer's birth year has been incorrectly ascribed.

Gerald Coke Handel Collection, accession no. 5215

⊹

43

42. The Charming Brute
Caricature engraving, hand coloured and published anonymously by Joseph Goupy; second issue, ca. 1754

42

This engraving depicting the composer's vast appetite by his friend is thought to have cost the artist a legacy in a codicil to the composer's will.

Gerald Coke Handel Collection, accession no. 5213

43. George Frideric Handel
Oil on canvas, attributed to William Hoare; ca. 1760

Gerald Coke Handel Collection, accession no. 5204

❖

44

44. Allegorical study for a memorial print
Oil on canvas by Giovanni Battista Cipriani, ca. 1760

Allegorical study with angels, a muse and putti holding a sheet with a portrait of Handel at the head of the score of 'Comfort ye, my people' from 'Messiah'. From the collection of Earl Howe, a descendent of Charles Jennens for whom it was probably painted to order with the idea that a commemoration print would be made from it; however, no engraving of this design has been traced.

Gerald Coke Handel Collection, accession no. 5224

✣

45

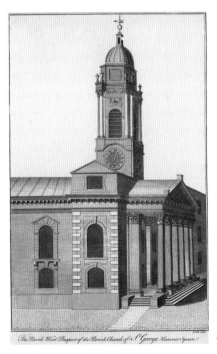

46

45. A View of the Foundling Hospital
Line engraving; ca. 1752

Gerald Coke Handel Collection, accession no. 5221

46. The North West Prospect of the Parish Church of St. George Hanover Square
Line engraving by B. Cole; ca. 1754

Handel was a parishioner at this church just a short walk from his house in Brook Street.

Gerald Coke Handel Collection, accession no. 5217

47

47. The North Prospect of St Andrew's Church in Holborn
Line engraving by B. Cole; 1754

The blind composer John Stanley was organist at this church where Thomas Coram is now buried. Stanley also directed performances at the Foundling Hospital.

Gerald Coke Handel Collection, accession no. 5216

48

48. Thomas Norris, Late Organist of Christ Church and St. John's College Oxford

Hand-coloured stipple engraving by John Taylor after his own drawing; 1791

Thomas Norris (1741-1790), tenor singer, sang in the Commemoration concerts of 1784.

Gerald Coke Handel Collection, accession no. 5226

49. Saml. Harrison

Soft-ground etching, proof state without lettering, by William Daniell after the portrait by George Dance; ca. 1814

Samuel Harrison (1760-1812), bass singer, sang in the Commemoration concerts of 1784.

Gerald Coke Handel Collection, accession no. 5228

49

50

50. Joah Bates
Soft-ground etching by William Daniell after the portrait by George Dance of 1794; 1809

Bates (1741-1799) conducted the Commemoration concerts of 1784; he was tutor and later private secretary to the 4th Earl of Sandwich.

Gerald Coke Handel Collection, accession no. 5227

51. Sir Watkin Williams Wynn, Bart
Drypoint portrait of Watkin Williams Wynn by Benjamin Wilson; ca. 1785

A great patron of the arts and an ardent Handelian, Wynn (1749-1789) was a director of the 1784 Commemoration festival concerts.

Loaned by Colin Coleman

51

❖

52. Charles Burney
Stipple engraving by Francesco Bartolozzi after the oil painting by Sir Joshua Reynolds (1723-1792) now in the National Portrait Gallery; 1784

Burney wrote the introductory essays to 'An Account of the Musical Performances in Westminster Abbey and the Pantheon, May 26th, 27th, 29th; and June the 3rd and 5th, 1784, in Commemoration of Handel'.

Gerald Coke Handel Collection, accession no. 5229

52

53

53. Commemoration of Handel : Fourth performance Thursday, June the 3rd
Programme book London: H. Reynell, 1784

Portraits of three of the four performers mentioned on this opening are displayed in this case. The contemporary owner has annotated the programme book where the performer's name has not been printed and on other pages has commented on the music and performance.

Gerald Coke Handel Collection, accession no. 5232

54. Madame Mara

Stipple engraving by William Ridley after the portrait by Jacques Louis David (1748-1825); 1800

Gertrud Elisabeth Mara (1749-1833) was the principal soprano soloist in the 1784 Commemoration concerts.

Gerald Coke Handel Collection, accession no. 5231

54

55. Concert admission ticket

Engraved by John Keyse Sherwin after a drawing by Biagio Rebecca (1735-1808); 1784

Handel's head is shown in profile within a wreath above a monument. This ticket was used for the performance at Westminster Abbey on 26 May 1784; on the verso it has been endorsed by Lord Sandwich (John Montagu (1718-1792)) for the use of the Duchess of Portland (Dorothy Cavendish (1750-1794), wife of the 3rd Duke of Portland).

55

Gerald Coke Handel Collection, accession no. 5230

56

56. Grand Musical Festival in Westminster-Abbey : Third performance, The Messiah. June the 6th
Programme book London: 1786.

Opened at the page showing the end of the list of members and subscribers, reporting the accounts of the Commemoration concerts of the previous year and the opening page of the words for the performance of 'Messiah'.

Loaned by Handel House Museum (Byrne collection) accession no. 1998.163

57. An account of the musical performances in Westminster-Abbey and the Pantheon, May 26th, 27th, 29th and June the 3d and 5th, 1784 in commemoration of Handel by Charles Burney
London: Printed for the Benefit of the Musical Fund, 1785

The performances were all patronised by the King and the events raised £6,000 for the Royal Society of Musicians, and £1,000 for the Westminster Hospital. The volume includes eight plates, showing entrance tickets, the orchestra plan and scenes of the performances. This particular picture by the author's nephew, Edward Francis Burney (1760-1848), is reproduced in a line engraving showing the special construction made for the performers and the audience in the Abbey.

Gerald Coke Handel Collection, accession no. 87

58. Draft letter from Charles Burney to Lord Sandwich
[London]: 27 Nov. 1784

The letter, written some months after the concerts, concerns the delay in producing Burney's published Account.

Gerald Coke Handel Collection, accession no. 3074

58 *with detail*

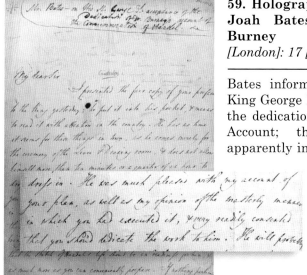

59 *with detail*

59. Holograph letter from Joah Bates to Charles Burney
[London]: 17 [July, 1784]

Bates informs Burney that King George III has accepted the dedication to him of the Account; the King was apparently involved with the compilation of the volume.

Loaned by the Royal Academy of Music

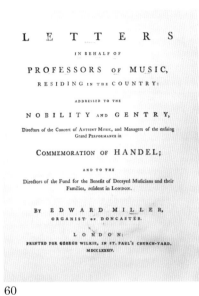

60

60. Letters in behalf of Professors of Music, Residing in the Country ... by Edward Miller
London, 1784

Members of the Society of Musicians had to reside some part of the year in London which Edward Miller felt discriminated against "country musicians", and at the time of the 1784 Commemoration concerts he called for a separate fund to be set up for those who lived entirely away from London. The result was the "New Musical Fund" established on 16 April 1786 which was to have an annual charity performance; the fund shared in the profits from the "Royal Musical Festival" of 1834 but was dissolved in 1842.

Loaned by Leeds Library and Information Services

61

61. Edward Miller
Stipple engraving by Thomas Hardy [Published by F. Linley, 1796]

Edward Miller (1735-1807) studied music with Charles Burney and during the 1750s played the flute in Handel's oratorio orchestra. The name Miller appears in the Foundling Hospital 'Messiah' benefit performances of 1754 and 1758 although as a trumpeter and may refer to a different performer.

Gerald Coke Handel Collection, accession no. 5203

❖

Terracotta model for Handel's monument in Westminster Abbey by Louis François Roubiliac, ca.1759

Gerald Coke Handel Collection, accession no. 5239

✣